Batman is one of the Super Friends.

Aquaman is king of the seas.

Captain Fear is a lost sailor.

Black Manta is a crook.

The Super Friends were at sea. Suddenly, an odd sound echoed around them.

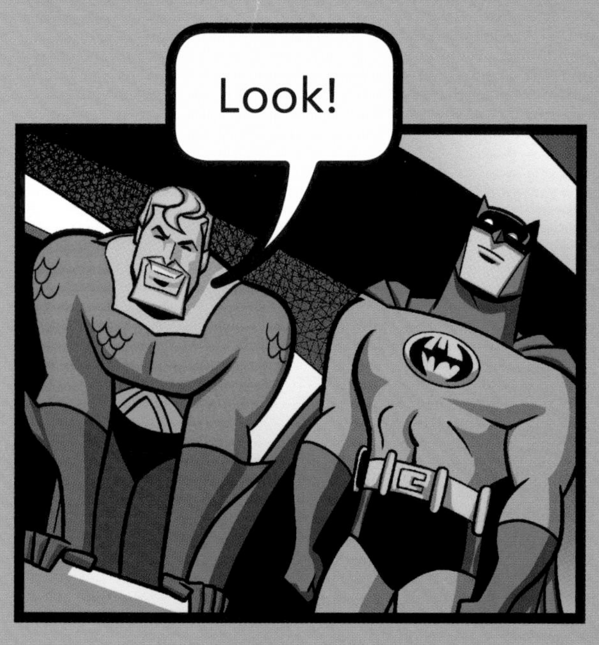

An old ship!
It’s a schooner.

I am Captain Fear.
A lost sailor?
Yes.
I was working on a ship.
I did some bad things.
Now a dark spell makes me roam the seas forever.
But you are kind now. You rescue ships!

We will help you!
How?

The Stone of Skood will stop the spell!
I do like a quest!

Hmm ...

Let’s go!

Can a stone really stop the spell?
Yes!

This way.
Through this rocky arch.

Where is the Stone of Skood?
Atlantis.
But Atlantis sank into a chasm!
Right! So there may be a few problems!

Like this?
Yes!
Look out!
I can stop it ...
... with echoes from my mind!
Maybe not!

Here it comes again!
Aquaman shot black squid ink at the sea monster.
Duck!
Crunch!
The sea monster is stuck now!
Good one!

Every quest has one or two problems!
Here is the next one ...
A whirlpool!
It is like a corkscrew!
Let me think ...
Hold on!
Quick!

I can make a disc.
The whirlpool will suck it down, while we go ...
... up!
Phew!

Not far now.
Look!

Is it ...?

Atlantis! Yes!

There is the Stone of Skood.

Once you pick up the stone, I am free from the spell!

Here goes!

Zap!
Crash!
Crack!

That will teach you!

Black Manta?
Yes!
The stone is mine and the spell stays.

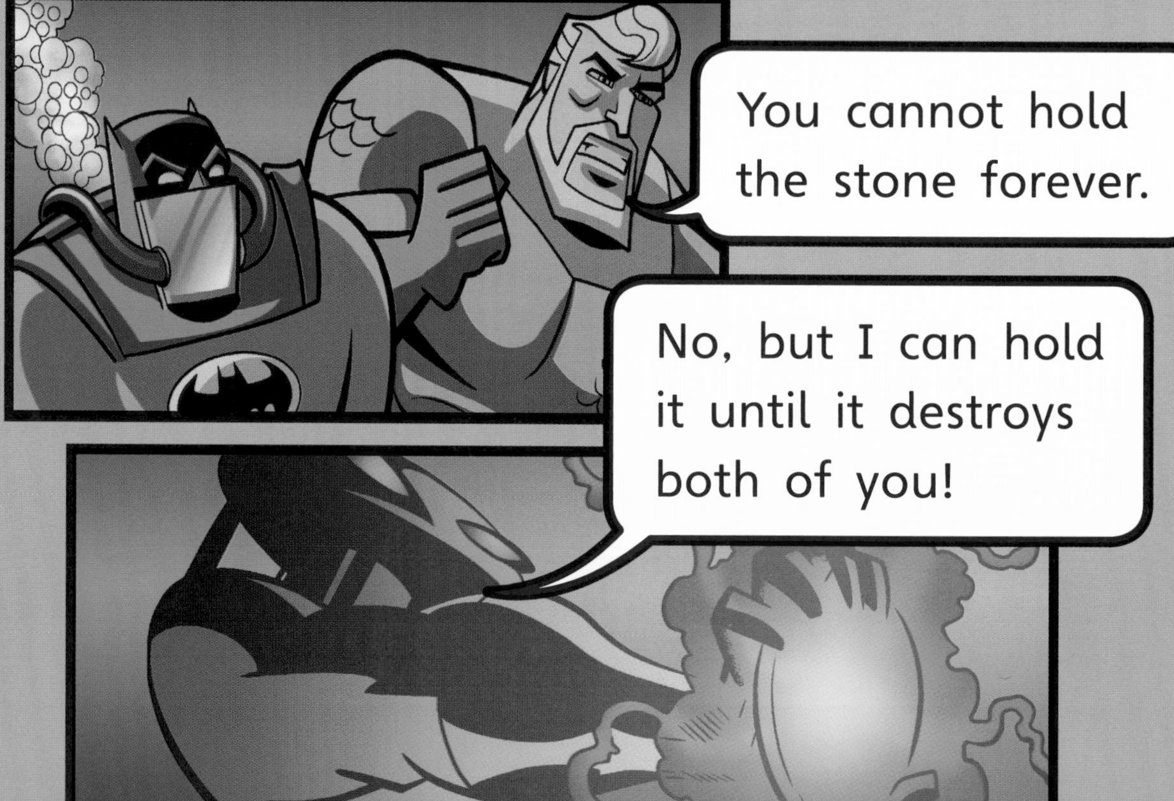
You cannot hold the stone forever.
No, but I can hold it until it destroys both of you!

Captain Fear hurls a rock at the stone.

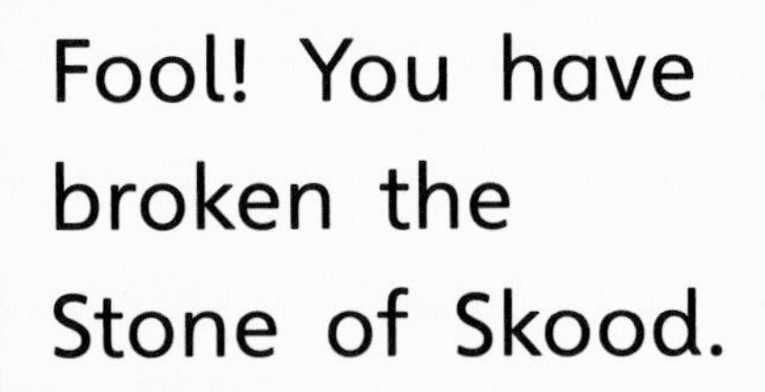

We cannot stop the spell.

But look! The spell is lifting!

Because you saved us!
I am free! Farewell!

The quest is complete.